W9-CQA-249

The Diary for Dreamers

To Rabbi Beliak
With best regards !
Diana
1985
Claremont

by Diana Lilley Smith

Distributed by

DREAM
      PRODUCTIONS
            UNLIMITED

1663 Lafayette Road
Claremont, CA 91711   (714) 624-5178

© 1978 by Diana Lilley Smith
Library of Congress Number 78-7074
International Standard Book Number 0-931862-00-0
Artwork Courtesy of Dover Publications Inc.

The Shoreline Press
A division of Brasch and Brasch, Publishers, Inc.
220A West "B" Street
Ontario, California 91762

for Lance Christian Smith
1960-1976
who dared to dream

Whose love, vibrance, and caring
was a joy to all whose
lives he touched

Somewhere beyond the
    rainbow . . .
        Harnessed to the
            brightest star.

INTRODUCTION

This book is a diary to be written in. Enjoy the fresh and original dream quotations created especially for it.

Though many persons profess not to dream, nor to be aware of their dreams, dreaming goes on subconsciously during sleep. It is the essence of our inner selves.

Dreams are an instrument through which you can discover resources within yourself which you did not know you possessed. The inner relationships of events in one's daily life often surface in dreams. Understanding their reality is a journey downward into one's subconscious. In order to become aware of your labyrinthine mind, begin by telling yourself that you want to recall your dreams.

In the recollecting and recording of one's dreams, this dream diary will provide a fascinating and valuable resource for personal growth and understanding. An exciting discovery is made that there are different levels of experience beneath the surface of your consciousness, and you will come to realize that you, alone, hold the key to potentialities that are ready to unfold.

Dreams provide a certain poetry, artistry, and beauty to the very things that may be lacking in one's everyday life. Night dreaming is essential as a release from one's tensions of the day. Without them, unreleased tensions are likely to spill over into the waking hours.

Dream symbols can be as individual as fingerprints. It is important in evaluating your dreams that you discover and identify your own personal symbols. These will occur regularly with your awareness, and their symbolic forms will be self-disclosing which will allow you to become your own dream interpreter. Symbolism in dreams is commonly found in the ancient and sacred writings of India, China, Egypt, and in the Old and New Testaments.

Dreams should be evaluated, however, rather than interpreted or censored. Being judgmental about one's dreams could be inhibiting. In recording dreams, your ego is revelaed through your deeper-than-conscious psyche which becomes the looking-glass that mirrors your mind and character.

If you feel out of tune with your inner-self, and your dreams are not fulfilling—experiment. Move your before-sleep thoughts ahead to a point in your life where you wish to be. Go down into your dreams with the courage to venture into undiscovered and unexplored spheres within yourself. Mentally picture which paths you wish to take, re-examine alternative avenues of pursuit, and reflect upon relationships you might like to develop.

By orienting yourself to move forward into the future within your dreams, it is possible to develop control, and to dream the dreams you want.

HOW TO USE THE DREAM DIARY

Keep a pad and pencil by your bed, so that you can make notations after you dream. If you awaken in the middle of the night, write down just such key words as will enable you to recall the dream in the morning. Otherwise, it could disappear and be completely lost from your mind. Try to catch the "tail-of-the-dream" before it slips away entirely.

Wake up slowly in the morning. Try to remember the scenes, the settings, the people. Your dreams may not return to your mind all at once, but as fragments, and small pieces of dreams. These are jotted down. Later, when you have some quiet reflective time, transfer these dreams to your Dream Diary. In writing in your diary, keep it simple. Record all dreams that you can recall. Recurrent dreams, and especially those from childhood, should be recorded. Date your dreams. If a dream seems particularly significant, plant a thought in your subconscious that you wish to pursue that dream again in your altered state of consciousness.

If you feel that you must interpret your dreams, try not to do so immediately. What might seem unimportant at the moment may, at a later date, prove to be of great significance and convey a completely different meaning.

Reread your dreams when relaxed. Allow your reveries to slip back over your dreams as a whole. This is in essence a meditative way of going into the depth process which is continually seeking to unfold within us.

PREFACE

If we keep a record of our dreams, we know where we are at all times; whether in a fantasy world . . . or reality. By doing this, we can benefit from and enjoy each day. As a *Tool*, we can use our dreams to show us the tomorrows . . . the todays . . . and the yesterdays.

We all have our own special symbols. Once we recognize, remember, and understand them, we will know whether we are progressing or faltering in our daily life.

Do you realize that your *Thoughts* are you . . . and what you *Really* are is portrayed to you in your dreams? The symbol of a bird or an airplane in your dreams indicates a desire or an urge for freedom, a break-through into higher creativity. This shows the person is becoming attuned to a greater, more expansive state of awareness.

Color in our dreams represents a developing sensitivity to inner states of awareness; also a signal that direct action is necessary. Color is energy in action. Color is soothing and healing. A particular color observed in a dream indicates the need to utilize that color as much as possible for a few days—in foods, in thought and in clothing, as well.

Everything creatively possible can first be introduced to you in a dream state. Once visualized, the formula for its completion is at your fingertips. Remember that thoughts, words and dreams are living things!

C.C. Bateman

[C.C. Bateman is an international lecturer and teacher on dreams and their symbols. His great sensitivity in the area of dreams has enabled him to help thousands of people to understand their dream world and to use the knowledge to construct a more rewarding life.]

Candy to the child
    Accomplishes the dream stanza.
Love to man and maiden
    Repeats the theme . . .
                                Rosemary Adam

Dreams

are

places

where

we

can

meet

people

we

can't

see

elsewhere.

Yehuda
Amichai

Dreams are love-children from
the matings of memory and
hope.

Dreams are cloud materials
that frame our higher
stars.
James W. Angell

Dreams are the skylines of distant cities on half-clear mornings.

Dreams both send us loping across the meadows of lost yesterdays, and elate us with the glimmerings of unarrived tomorrows.

James W. Angell

Although awake, I oft dream dreams,
Not night dreams full of nightmare screams
But daydreams, which I always find
Dreams of a very pleasant kind.

My dreams don't come true,
But, my nightmares do!
Richard Armour

Dreams are your yardstick to measure
your progress upon the path, and
your reception to the higher
impressions.
C.C. Bateman

Thoughts vanish into empty nothingness. Have the sensations ceased? Silent memories remain from my dreams, as well as the knowledge of the inevitable...

Susie Berg

13

Fears, wishes, conflicts, but more inspiration
and the creative force itself—these are
what our dreams are made of.

Know your dreams, and you will know
your deepest fears, wishes, and
conflicts. But in the end,
you will also know God.
Harold H. Bloomfield

I have often wondered which part
creates the real dream: sleep
or the waking state.

David E. Bresler

Nightmares are friendly warnings, delivered with a power sure to ensure our close attention . . .

cocktail party attended by the personalities who reside inside us . . . *David Bresler*

A dream is a

Dreams not only get us through the night,
They get us through the day!
Put them together with your real expericences,
And you have a complete life.

Helen Gurley Brown

Dreams are the mind's expression of what the
conscious cannot or will not express.
All that night-time dancing
makes daytime walking more enjoyable.

Helen Gurley Brown

Generally I keep my dreams
Separate from my realities.
But on occasion,
I let the two merge . . .
Lynn Butler

doesn't please, one can retreat and dream another one . . . *Margaret Dill Cantley*

Daydream dialogues are very satisfactory, because if the ending

Today we share the dreams of tomorrow,
Sifting through our puzzled thoughts.
Drifting high and drifting so low,
All our dreams have something taught . . .

An idea pressed through an ordinary mind,
Is a dream in a funny sort of way.
A person thinks and tries to find
Future messages to end the day.

Connie Susan Care

Dreams fulfilled may not be good . . .
  Especially if we don't dream what
    we should.

Donald K. Cheek

Dreams are messages from your subconscious
written by your guides to help you
solve the riddles of your life.
Florence Cohn

But, we are all richer for the dreams we've had . . . *Jeffrey E. Corey*

Dreams can be fun or scary—good or bad!

Dreams are as ephemeral as a sand castle on a hot summer beach,
Or as durable as a medieval castle basking in the piercing sun.
Our dreams, chimerical or pragmatic, are worth fortunes or nothing at all—
It all depends upon how dearly one wants fantasies to become realities.

Jane Ellen Cross

Reality

    can

        be

           "dream-like"

               when

                  explored

                    by

                       a

                          creative

                            imagination.

Phil Dike

Dreams

are

like

patterns

left

free

to

explore

unpredictable

journeys . . .

Phil Dike

Dreams are the fruit of life,
For without dreams,
Life is just a bowl of pits.

James V. Doiron

Dreams are the winds of
our imagination that
free us from the reality
of life.

Christine Anne Escovedo

Dreams

    reflect

        emotions

           in

              the

                  shadows

                     of

                         life

                           and

                        mind . . .

Frederick O. Flye

Dreams that are not remembered,
were probably best forgotten.
Mark W. Foresman

In our hearts—in our minds—dreams are past imaginings and future foretellings.

Sue Anne Gatten

Dreams knock at the door of consciousness.
Who knows what will answer?
Joan Giles

Through

   the

      gateways

         of

            dream

               we

                  enter

                     to

                        remember

                           the

                            future,

                               to

                                see

                                   our

                                     evergreen

                                     tomorrows . . .

Francoise Gilot

Hands across the sea . . . it's a brave
and lofty theme.
An yet, what of one who merely dips
a toe—and dreams?
William R. Graydon

Often, to run is to dream,
    To lose oneself in the sound of your own footfalls,
To return replenished to the realm of reality.
                                    Jacqueline Hansen

Dreams, like the opening and closing of a
window, give us views in the night . . .

Greg Handziak

My dreams are leads and intimations
of what is being unfolded by the
acorn that knows my oak tree.
Frances Heussenstamm

I

dreamed

I

caught

the

love

bouquet

and

watched

as

it

grew

many

blossoms.

Susan Kimberly Hyde

If all my dreams would come true,
Then I'd dream the whole night through!
Diann Jackson

Today's dreams may become
tomorrow's realities.
Barrie Marie Johnson

Soothing - calming

Expressing feelings of oneself . . .

Dreams are the

necessary respite from tedium

Christopher L. Johnson

When I keep dreaming, I can find
any possibility to be happy.
Once I stop dreaming, I can't
find even a hope in my life.
Machiko Kaida

Live for today, but dream for tomorrow . . . *Jamie Sue Kennedy*

Dreaming

    dreams

        is

            like

                flowing

                    sap

                        in

                          a

                            growing

                              tree . . .

Eugene Kovalenko

Remembering dreams is like cultivating
seeds whose fruit can satisfy the
hunger for God and inner peace . . .

Sharing dreams is like harvesting the tree of life in a celebration feast
on the road towards outer peace . . .
Eugene Kovalenko

People living in peace,
Giving respect to nature,
The two, as one, working together,
and someone's dreams make it real.

Jeffrey A. Kozlovich

Take
heed
in
your
dreams
for
they
may
come
true.
William L.
Kreeger

The wise are said to examine their dreams, the poor to enjoy them; but the ones who succeed listen to their dreams, because they are the Word of God . . . *William L. Kreeger*

I'm waiting in the wings, alone
My friend has gone on stage, and left
Now I'm here, not on, not off,
Alone!

Barry Lank

Dreams are the carapace
that cauterize my hurt . . .
Uelaine Lengefeld

Dreams are like flowers that
    bud in the night—
Blooming . . . full of promise . . .
    waiting for the light.

A budding young artist's dream
    of grandeur and fame . . .
is to paint an immortal picture,
    signed with his name . . .
                        Lillian Lilley

I view my dreams with awe and reverence for
they speak to me of myself as if I were
looking into a mirror at all that I am, was,
and ever will be.
Marianne Lindgren

Dreams are the occasions when we can do whatever we want, without the judgment of others . . . *Randal S. Mason*

My constant daytime thoughts, it seems
Bring cherished visions in my dreams.
Frank McCarthy

fantasies, and visions of our endings—these are our dreams, and we live through all of them . . . *Paul C. McDonald*

Wild, imaginative images, glorious

Dreams bring nostalgic reverie
of past loves.

Dreams are butterflies from the
cocoons of our subconscious.
Shirley McDowell

Dreams catapult arrows of intense emotion through the dark toward the citadel of our sanity . . . . *Shirley McDowell*

The most exciting dream is one
that remains to become the core of
a creative thought.

Some dreams linger to solidify
into action, others vanish into space.
Harrison McIntosh

If I could,
I would . . .
Daydream your nighttime
sorrows away . . .

Dreams

are

made

of

moonbeams

fair,

angels

hair,

and

fluff.

Christina Monterastelli

60

Dreams half-remembered and unrecorded
are lost works of art.
Robert E. Morsberger

What man is not by nature,
he can by dreams become.
Afton Dill Nance

Dreams are freedom's thoughts.
They come without threat of
repression and flow with-
out fear of restraint.
Anita Natale

63

Most dreams have been forgotten,
but some have been remembered
and are kept in the heart
along with other beautiful memories.
Janet Elaine Nelson

We

are

all

the

creations

of

our

dreams.

Roy C.
Nelson

Dreaming is to creativity
What romance is to marriage;
Without it, nothing gets started!
Helen Nielsen

Dreams make strange bedfellows. - - - *Darcy O'Brien*

shine if you keep an eye on them. But, if you stop caring about them, then they will cease to exist . . .

Wendy Ann Ogle

Dreams are like stars. They will sparkle and

Dreams are the fantasies of life . . .
They make the realistic, and enhance the fantastic.
Julie Ohman

Afloat in a dream all my own . . .
You may be a part of it,
But you are not welcomed.
Robyn Olson

We float on airy clouds,
And journey to the pits of hell
All that can and cannot be comes true . . .
Then we return, once more, to the dream.
Christopher C. Peterson

he didn't get the chance to fulfill them . . . A fact—a cold hard fact—which doesn't seem just. *John Pixley*

He had his dreams like everyone of us. But,

Wooden ghosts hobble through
the graveyard of my dreams.

Some dreams are strange friends,
and friendly strangers.
John D. Quinlan

Sometimes in the wee hours, thin dreams
slip gently between you and your
mattress . . . in them I am hidden.

And the mountain streams are filled with dreams,
but, we dare not imbibe lest realities die.

Everything you really are, you have always been.
    It is just a matter of getting in touch
        with your dreams.
    John D. Quinlan

Dreams fill the night
with distorted images of
the day's happenings.
Cathy Roberts

75

Whenever I have a real conflict, and am undecided
about the choice I have to take in life, I simply
ask for an answer in my dreams—and sure enough
the dream reveals in what direction I have to go.
Elisabeth Kubler-Ross

Reality of dreams is made . . . *Jonas Salk*

Dreams

are

what

you

would

want

to

have

your

life

like . . .

Brett Schroeder

Lucy speaking to Charlie Brown - "Your dreams are messages that
your brain is trying to send to prepare you for the days that
follow."
Charlie Brown comments - "Even my brain is against me."

Charles M. Schulz

Dreams and realities don't have
to be two different things.
Bowen N. Smith

Nightdreams meld into daydreams
like star-crossed lovers, leaving
behind illusions of wholeness and
bittersweet happiness—spilling
out timelessness . . .
Diana Lilley Smith

Today's memories begin with last night's dreams.
Noel S. Smith

Keep a little sheltered space within
your heart for secret dreams to go.

Invisible rainbows

encircle our lives - permeate our dreams - lending color, everlastingly . . .

Diana Lilley Smith

The life I live is fiction,
the dreams I have are truth.
William Stafford

I have my dreams and
so I live in paradise
and walk with God.
Gerald B. Stiles

Dreams are the windows that let you peek into fantasy . . .

Susan Trent

The statement that "truth is stranger than fiction" must have come from a dreamer returning to reality.

Edmund Van Deusen

Dreams can briefly born us from the confining womb
of ordinary reality, giving us glimpses into a
wondrous world beyond.

Jeanne Walker

We still dream; we know dreams' true purpose.
Dreams soar us to heights of self, known
through increasingly unbroken union
with the Supreme.
Karen Walker

To still dreams we know realms true-life has
Allows us not to sample of self-known
Such meanings whenfrom quiet
With theiranswers.

To dream
is to
open
your mind
to the
good things
in life,
for what
is life
if you
cannot
dream? . . .

Krystal Webb

To go to that place where I am free to be me, where freedom and peace prevail; that is my dream . . .

Krystal Webb

91

If all my dreams came true,
what would be left
to hope for?
Lisa Whale

I planted a seed last night,
And, it grew into a dream.

Pierced ideas - crying sighs.
Shattered ladder . . .
Dreams sometimes die.

Laura Wilson

ACKNOWLEDGEMENTS

It is my happy duty to acknowledge that the preparation of this book has been made possible only by the generosity and sensitivity of Claremont High School students and teachers, friends, and others who contributed the dream quotations.

Special thanks to Elisabeth Kubler-Ross and Cathy Leone for their love and encouragement, and especially to my husband, Bowen Smith, who contributed numerous suggestions in the development of this book.

The intuitive understanding, practical suggestions, and assistance of significant others deserves more than gratitude.

DIANA LILLEY SMITH

MAY 1978
CLAREMONT, CALIFORNIA

ABOUT THE DREAMERS

ROSEMARY ADAM, English teacher, Claremont High School (Claremont, California)

YEHUDA AMICHAI, Israeli poet.

JAMES W. ANGELL, Presbyterian minister and author.

RICHARD ARMOUR, PH.D., humorist, lecturer, and author of over fifty books.

C.C. BATEMAN, Lecturer on dreams and author; president of Dream Counsellors, Inc., and member of American Medical Psychic Research.

SUSIE BERG, Senior, Claremont High School.

HAROLD H. BLOOMFIELD, M.D., Psychiatrist and author. Director of Psychiatry, Institute of Psychophysiological Medicine, San Diego.

DAVID E. BRESLER, PH.D., Director of the Pain Control Unit, University of California Hospital and Clinics, Los Angeles.

HELEN GURLEY BROWN, Author, and editor of *Cosmopolitan*.

LYNN BUTLER, Senior, Claremont High School.

MARGARET DILL CANTLEY, Educator.

CONNIE SUSAN CARE, Senior, Claremont High School.

DONALD K. CHEEK, Ph.D., Professor of Psychology, California State Polytechnic University (San Luis Obispo, California).

FLORENCE COHN, Realtor and Business executive.

JEFFERY E. COREY, Senior, Claremont High School.

JANE ELLEN CROSS, Student, University of California at Davis, majoring in international relations.

PHIL DIKE, Watercolorist.

JAMES V. DOIRON, Senior, Claremont High School.

CHRISTINE ANNE ESCOVEDO, Senior, Claremont High School.

FREDERICK O. FLYE, Student, San Diego State University, majoring in engineering.

MARK W. FORESMAN, Senior, Claremont High School.

JOAN GILES, Writer and teacher.

FRANCOISE GILOT, Internationally-known painter and author.

WILLIAM R. GRAYDON, Publicist and author.

GREG HANDZIAK, Senior, Claremont High School.

JACQUELINE HANSEN, World Class Marathoner.

FRANCES HEUSSENSTAMM, Ph.D. Psychotherapist, Center for Counseling and Psychotherapy, Santa Monica; and teacher of the "Journal Process" at UCLA.

SUSAN KIMBERLY HYDE, Student, Chaffey College, majoring in journalism.

DIANN JACKSON, Senior, Claremont High School.

BARRIE MARIE JOHNSON, Senior, Claremont High School.

CHRISTOPHER L. JOHNSON, Senior, Claremont High School.

MACHIKO KAIDA, Student, University of Tokyo, majoring in education.

JAMIE SUE KENNEDY, Senior, Claremont High School.

EUGENE KOVALENKO, Ph.D., Scientist, teacher, poet, and singer.

JEFFREY A. KOZLOVICH, Student, California State Polytechnic University (Pomona, California).

WILLIAM L. KREEGER, Senior, Claremont High School.

BARRY LANK, Student, San Francisco State University, majoring in creative writing.

UELAINE LENGEFELD, Literature teacher, Claremont High School.

LILLIAN LILLEY, Musician-composer.

MARIANNE LINDGREN, Artist, musician, and anthropology major at University of California at Riverside.

RANDAL S. MASON, Senior, Claremont High School.

FRANK MCCARTHY, Film-maker and producer-director.

PAUL C. MCDONALD, Senior, Claremont High School.

SHIRLEY MCDOWELL, Opthalmic and biofeedback technician.

HARRISON MCINTOSH, Ceramist.

CHRISTINA MONTERASTELLI, Teacher of Yoga and mystical studies.

ROBERT E. MORSBERGER, Ph.D., Author, short-story writer, and Professor of English and Modern Languages, California State Polytechnic University at Pomona.

AFTON DILL NANCE, Former assistant state superintendent of schools, California State Department of Education, Sacramento, California.

ANITA NATALE, Student, University of the Pacific, majoring in recreational education.

JANET ELAINE NELSON, Senior, Claremont High School.

ROY C. NELSON, Senior, Claremont High School.

HELEN NIELSEN, Mystery story novelist and author of numerous movie and television scripts.

DARCY O'BRIEN, Ph.D., Novelist and Professor of English, Pomona College.

WENDY ANN OGLE, Senior, Claremont High School.

JULIE OHMAN, Student, Ricks College.

ROBYN OLSON, Student, San Diego State University, majoring in sociology.

CHRISTOPHER C. PETERSON, Student, University of California at Santa Cruz, majoring in art.

JOHN PIXLEY, Junior, Claremont High School.

JOHN D. QUINLAN, Business executive.

CATHY ROBERTS, Senior, Claremont High School.

ELISABETH KUBLER-ROSS, M.D., Psychiatrist, lecturer and author.

JONAS SALK, M.D., Director of the Salk Institute (La Jolla, California).

BRETT SCHROEDER, Student, American River College.

CHARLES M. SCHULZ, Syndicated cartoonist.

BOWEN N. SMITH, Colonel, U.S. Army, retired.

DIANA LILLEY SMITH, Writer and real estate broker.

NOEL S. SMITH, D.D.S., Dentist.

WILLIAM STAFFORD, Ph.D., Poet, Professor at Lewis and Clark College.

GERALD B. STILES, M.D., Surgeon.

SUSAN ALICE TRENT, Senior, Claremont High School.

EDMUND VAN DUESEN, Writer and sculptor.

JEANNE WALKER, Author and professor of English Literature and Composition, Chaffey College.

KAREN WALKER, daughter of Jeanne Walker.

KRYSTAL WEBB, Student, Mount San Antonio College, majoring in nursing.

LISA WHALE, Senior, Claremont High School.

LAURA JEAN WILSON, Senior, Claremont High School.